HOUGHTON MIFFLIN
Reading
A Legacy of Literacy

Look at
Us!

HOUGHTON MIFFLIN   BOSTON • MORRIS PLAINS, NJ

California • Colorado • Georgia • Illinois • New Jersey • Texas

Printed in the U.S.A.

ISBN: 0-618-16187-2

3456789-BS-06 05 04 03 02

Design, Art Management, and Page Production: Studio Goodwin Sturges

Contents

We Go to School

by Susan Gorman-Howe

illustrated by Maryann Cocca-Leffler

3

5

See What We Can Do

by Susan Gorman-Howe
illustrated by Sue Dennen

We Can Make It

by Susan Gorman-Howe
illustrated by Anthony Lewis

20

23